confessions of a
belly dancing sofa

confessions of a
belly dancing sofa

Sahfa Aboudkhil

First paperback edition: March 2022
Paperback ISBN: 9781956525298

Belly Dancing Sofa
Books to Hook Publishing, LLC.
United States

www.bellydancingsofa.wordpress.com

To Hannah,
All my love.
♡ -Sahla

To my dad for his love of stories. To my mom for her limitless love of mine. And to my sisters for no reason at all.

contents

intro 2

day 1 6

day 2 10

day 3 14

day 4 18

day 5 22

day 6 26

day 7 30

day 8 34

day 9 38

day 10 42

day 11 46

day 12 50

day 13 54

day 14 58

day 15 62

day 16 66

day 17 70

day 18 74

day 19 78

day 20 82

day 21 86

day 22 88

day 23 94

day 24 98

day 25 102

day 26 106

day 27 110

day 28 114

day 29 118

day 30 122

Sahfa Aboudkhil

Sahfa Aboudkhil

intro

confessions of a belly dancing sofa

I'm pretty much out of it now. But the event that was the first two years of my college has left its mark on me. I'm still marked by some kind of regret. Not that it happened, and not that it ended. I just wish I had more to show for it.

So, for a month, I'm going to say everything I can.
By the end of it, if the feeling is still with me, I'll
know it was something else all this time.

day 1

I wrote something a week ago. It took a lot out of
me, which is usually the case nowadays. It used to
be so hard to sit at the piano. I couldn't get a word
out without crying. It felt like they were all gone.
It's funny because, before, I didn't sing my own
lyrics most of the time. At my 'most creative'
I wasn't writing much at all.

The words from before were nothing like mine.
They were morbid, mysterious, psychedelic. I
loved that, then. I wanted people to find me that
way. I wanted to look in the mirror and see an
enigma. I did see that for a while. That's one of
the shared qualities of cults. It's a shared reality.
When you get a group of people together, and you
get everyone to believe the same thing, i.e. Dark
Chocolate is Poisonous, it can last quite a while.
But eventually, reality catches up. Something
falters, someone accidentally eats dark chocolate.
They don't die, and the whole thing cracks as
easily as an eggshell. It's so easy come, easy go.

.

day 2

confessions of a belly dancing sofa

For all the lows, and all the highs. I told a therapist once that I didn't experience a single low for two years. He probably didn't believe me, but it was true. It was like being high all the time. During that time, every problem I'd ever had disappeared. I remember saying I used to have so many insecurities, and wondered where they all went so fast. That shouldn't have been a relief. It should have been a warning.

If someone came to you and promised I can make
you never feel hungry again, would you do it?
Your mom tells you that your face has sunken in.
She says you've been fainting, and you have to
eat. She's not evil, just unenlightened. You calmly
tell her she's wrong. You've never felt better. The
come down was so hard. The consequences of that
time lasted longer than it did. The worst was the
return of something I hadn't felt since that
promise. It was a lingering feeling of starvation.

day 3

confessions of a belly dancing sofa

I remember crying a lot. I don't cry much anymore, but I actually miss it. I miss the way things burned. That's what's really insidious about depression. It fights to stay alive inside you. Even now, out of it, I'm called back. It can happen at the mall, like if I see a dress I would've worn back then. I look at that dress too long and the grief comes again.

It feels so much sexier to grieve than it does to grow. For a long time, I didn't get better simply because I didn't want to. I had a distinct, crazy thought. I don't want to get better. I want to be tragic. Of course, when in it, you don't think that's what you're doing. It's not that I wanted to be unhappy. I just didn't think moving on would help me at all. I wanted my old life back. To some extent, I was right. Happiness is not sexy. It's mundane and repetitive. And it's warm, not hot. The burn still comes, if you want it. It just doesn't take down the whole building.

day 4

I had a huge breakdown in my living room once
after a conversation with an ex-boyfriend. I was
trying to expel him. We weren't together, and he
wouldn't let me cut the tie. He let himself into my
apartment while I screamed at him to leave. Then
he sat on the kitchen floor and woefully looked at
me in an exaggerated way, looking down, to the
side, then back at me. He looked like a cartoon.

There are two kinds of people who don't feel empathy. The first you can spot quickly. They ask offbeat questions like why can't you just move on? They mimic human emotion the way they've seen it, like in cartoons. This one is easy to get over, since there's no real illusion of connection. They just don't know better. The second is the one who knows. That's who I was dealing with before, and who I'm still dealing with now.

day 5

When I meet new people I don't know where to start. I used to throw up all over them. Too many details, too quickly. I thought if I shared everything fast enough I could make them care, or understand.

It didn't go very well. If someone begs you to respect them, you won't. If someone tells you how kind they are, it doesn't feel true. Then there's people who readily talk about their trauma. We're more inclined to feel sorry for someone who never mentions it. I learned to keep it to myself. At a party months later, a friend asked me how can you say you were meant to sing when you never do? It seemed she'd been mustering up some courage to ask. I had to muster all mine up not to tell her.

day 6

confessions of a belly dancing sofa

27

Must've mistaken me for a good girl. I like to tell my parents I was born a liar. I joke that I can't help it. I've lied about big and small things. I've lied about love.

I made so many mistakes. When you're in a
situation, by virtue of you being there, you've
made at least one decision of your own. It's
important to recognize what fault looks like. If
you're in a car with a bad driver, and you crash,
that's not your fault. But if you get in again
because you like the way they drive, then, me too.
I have no small share of fault in my story. I chose
to get in many, many times.

day 7

confessions of a belly dancing sofa

It's bizarre to live something you believe no one could ever understand. It's lonely, and it's also not logical. There are so many people in the world. Something has to give.

You're never alone and here's why. Your problems aren't all that unusual. Someone had them before you, and they got over it. You can too.

day 8

confessions of a belly dancing sofa

I wish I could go back. I still really do.
It's so frustrating because I'm good now. This is
supposed to be when it ends. But it doesn't seem
to matter how far away I get, or how much
healthier. I would still go back to those two years.
I would do it all again.

I hoped I'd never say that. Or after all this time,
I'd have something more hopeful to say. Here it is.
Just because I would, doesn't mean that I have. It's
impossible to go back in time, but there are other
ways to permanently ease the ache. Every day that
I don't ease it is a victory. I win when I breathe.
I win in my sleep, even when I dream of the past.
I win, again and again, in every moment. I go on
even when my mind screams to go back.

day 9

confessions of a belly dancing sofa

When you're a singer, everything about you has to seem attractive: the way you move your mouth, the things you say to people after the show, and most of all, your hook. After everything happened I no longer had one. Overnight, this is who I am became this is what I used to do. There's nothing quite as debilitating as having nothing going for you. I felt so ugly. I felt like I had nothing to offer men anymore.

I started obsessing over the stuff I could control. I looked up my name and repeatedly clicked on links I wanted to show up if someone searched for me. I was trying to raise the traffic so they wouldn't get pushed down. It was useless. Most of the stuff the band made wasn't even online. I had two choices. I could continue down this clearly futile and insanity-inducing path. Or, I could stop. Instead of trying to resurrect it, I could cut out anything that reminded me of the band. That meant the obvious like rewatching our videos. But it also meant cutting out music, since it was a big trigger. For the next year, I avoided music like heartbreak. I didn't touch a single instrument. I didn't listen to a single song.

day 10

confessions of a belly dancing sofa

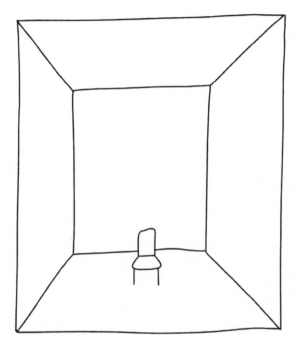

Eventually, I had to try again. I sat in a practice room and forced myself to write a song. In it, I said I knew I'd miss the stage because I didn't get enough. For so long I believed I wasn't supposed to be done yet. I didn't know how things went so wrong. I kept waiting to be saved. I wondered where religion fit into all of it and then I tried to blame god. Cosmically-flavored victim mentality, but I already had so much of the regular kind. I tried working with other people again. I spent weird nights sitting on a producer's bed, trying not to cry, coming up with the stupidest lyrics, saying whatever you think works best fifteen times, and then going home with someone who would inevitably ask me again that night why I was still crying. It was like hitting my head over and over. Smacking salt in a wound that wouldn't close.

The worst was the quiet in my head. I had all the means to get back into music, but I couldn't do it. I knew why. I knew my paralysis had nothing to do with music. It was about something deeper. It always had been. It's why I fell so hard in the first place.

day 11

confessions of a belly dancing sofa

I wish I had done things differently. I wish things happened for a reason. There seem to be no rules for anything. It's so random. The whole thing feels insane.

Some days are better than others. It comes in
waves. I think we go around trying to find relief.
We want to stop being uneasy. We find a quick
fix. It's usually a person, but it can be a purpose. I
wonder if I ever liked music that much. Maybe I
just liked having some control. The wave again.
I've learned to hold my breath and let it flow
over me.

day 12

confessions of a belly dancing sofa

I think a lot about the idea that we're afraid of our own greatness. I've decided it's a generous way to describe insecurity.

That's how my friend was. Deeply insecure. I
know that, now, and I forgive him. It's why he
learned to be so good with people. His brain
hadn't produced its own validation in so long. He
had to coax it from other people to survive. I saw
it in his eyes sometimes. He was tired. He'd
indulged it too long. I tell my sisters all the time.
If there's one thing I want from you, it's to be
cocky. I want you to be so confident that
insecurity can't touch you. Because when it slips
in, you'll indulge it. You'll steal compliments to
feed it. You'll get tired and then it'll take over.

day 13

confessions of a belly dancing sofa

I'm struggling today. I can't decide how much
to write about the good parts. I really want to. I
want to talk about the band, and the magic of
our friendship. It's a beautiful story. We were
all so close. There were no walls between us.
We spent every day together. Laughing at each
other, laughing until the next morning. We fell
asleep intertwined in twin beds. We thought we
would live together after college.

It helps to remember the fairytale. It reminds me it wasn't wasted time. But I need to remember the bad more. I have to relive it or I'll ignore the horror movie parts again. I'm not dumb. I knew something was very off. I saw the warnings and I closed my eyes. Kind of like a girl in a movie when something is moving in on her. My family and friends were screaming at the TV. Except I didn't care what happened to me, as long as I could stay forever.

day 14

The healing process starts when you're finally honest with yourself. It's not something that comes naturally, especially because I prefer to lie.

I've done so much of the work already. I'm going to heal from this story soon. But I have to tell it first. This is my victory lap. I'll run around once and then I'll come back for the people I left behind.

day 15

confessions of a belly dancing sofa

I learned pretty early I wasn't gorgeous. When I
was younger I picked up on the context clues.
Adults liked to spell it out so I didn't miss it. I
wasn't terrible. I just wasn't a beauty everyone
agreed on. It ate me up constantly. I never made
peace with it. When I got to college, things got
better. I was getting some attention. And I met
this guy at a jam session my first week. We
decided to start a band. He quickly became my
best friend, and my biggest admirer. He had a
way of saying things like facts. You're a
goddess, he told me. No one compares. I trusted
him completely, so, for the next two years
I didn't think it for myself. I looked in my
mirror and heard his voice.

When I got sick, I clung to men like life rafts. I had to find someone new to convince me I was beautiful. I had this belief. If I were more beautiful I would've made it. Essentially, only supermodels can be successful. Since getting better, beauty has become my favorite topic of conversation. I tell anyone who will listen. People will always treat you based on your looks. That's true. But it's subjective, which means there's a window of time before they decide if you're beautiful or not. So, make the decision for them. It's easier to go with the tide than against it. Let people agree with you that you're beautiful. They'd rather do that, anyway.

day 16

confessions of a belly dancing sofa

My friend was really charming. I later told a therapist if she met him, she'd love him. He was the most intelligent person I'd ever met. And he was a learned pick-up artist. That's the art of picking up women. We'd often discuss his last guest over dinner. He'd tell me how he got them. Sometimes, it was the right compliment. Or he established ease by moving locations with them. Or he paid extra attention to their friend so they'd get jealous and leap at him when he finally turned it back. When one of the girls complained, I spoke for him. You think he made you uncomfortable? You were flirting right back. I called it loyalty. She called it like it was, and we never saw her again.

I saw a documentary after about a couple whose neighbor kidnapped their daughter, twice. They described how charming he was. They'd trusted him and were so ashamed. I remember how I felt it way deep in my stomach. At the time it was something I really related to. I was nowhere near their situation, but I was ashamed of how I treated that girl. I went online looking for responses from the audience. I thought I would find evidence they could be reasonable after the couple explained themselves. I thought people would understand. Instead I found hundreds of how could they fall for that, they're terrible parents, they're just as sick as him. I walked to the bathroom and threw up.

day 17

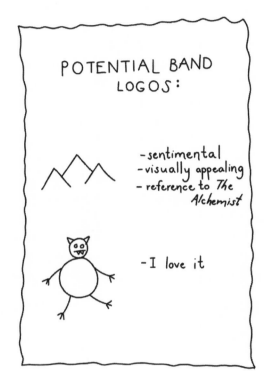

Fame, fortune, and bitches was the name of our group chat. That was my work. The band name was mine, too. It's a reference to my favorite book- a story about pursuing your personal treasure. Ours was the pursuit of music. We played on the street, at school, in apartments, in frat houses. We even played on Sunset Boulevard. Yesterday, I found a video of our Halloween show. We'd impulsively bought a fog machine and set it up in the middle of this huge parking garage. Someone turned it on for soundcheck, and all the fire alarms went off. We moved out while laughing about who would take the blame. The police car came and went and we put the show on an hour later.

It was a performance I remember going really
well. Last night I couldn't even sit through one
song. Where was the greatest band in the world?
This surely couldn't be it. Even I sounded bad.
Near the end I started really dreading rehearsals.
Every time I sang I heard dissonance. It was like
one of the instruments was permanently out of
tune. I started getting severe about it. I called out
one of my bandmates at a show, and stopped the
song to tell him he wasn't in tune. It didn't seem
to matter how much time we spent tuning pre-
show or during. Something wasn't sounding right.

day 18

In the process of healing I became a little self-victim-blamey. I had to believe I was stronger now and wouldn't be manipulated like that again. With it comes the implication I was weak before. I think there's truth to that. I was dealing with a lot of insecurity. Any girl coming out of high school can say the same. My dad disagrees. He says I wouldn't tell a child they were weak for being bullied, which is true. I wouldn't say it to their face.

The answer is somewhere in the middle. It's important to know it wasn't your fault. Still, you're the one in charge of getting better. In order to do that you have to believe you have control over your situation. I find control in little things. For example, I divide my timeline in two. First, my weak straight hair phase, and now, my strong curly hair phase. It helps to attach my internal growth to something physical. I'll do that until I get traumatized again and have to designate a third, bald head phase.

day 19

confessions of a belly dancing sofa

I keep getting older and more scared. I used to be so fearless. If you ask anyone from high school, they'd call it obnoxious. At my freshman year talent show I had a sore throat and screeched my song right into the microphone. My parents told me how awful it was on the silent drive home. When I was a sophomore, I gave a speech at a rally wearing these tight red leggings. Turns out the rally was on the gym floor and I was standing above seated middle schoolers who, by the way, totally took pictures. In my senior year I ran for president and lost in the most humiliating way. A lot of my high school experience felt like that nightmare where you forget to wear clothes and the whole school laughs at you.

And when I'm unhealthy, all those memories
come back. It's like having to fight the same
battles, over and over again. I'm not sure when
that ends completely. I do know there's a huge
benefit to writing about it. I get to revisit my past,
but this time, as a storyteller. It's an incredible
feeling. I can't wait to write the rest of it.

day 20

confessions of a belly dancing sofa

I remember when the disillusionment started. Almost at the end, when things were already unraveling, my friend gave me Steven Tyler's autobiography. It was his Bible. He used to call me the Steven Tyler to his Joe Perry. He always referenced the book, but he never wanted us to read it. So when he said you can read this now, I jumped. I'll never forget the feeling when I read the first line. Somehow it was already familiar. It was like a memory I couldn't place. The realization hit me like a bus. I recognized it because for the past two years, every word that came out of his mouth came directly from those pages. His philosophies, his life experiences, his catchphrases, and his entire persona, all were Steven Tyler's. I'd been friends with a made-up character.

He told us once about a time he got in trouble in elementary school. He used to tell his classmates stories. He could talk a new universe into existence. He really had a gift. One day, he started making a game out of it. It was like a choose-your-own-adventure, but it was on the playground, and he was charging money for it. If they wanted to buy a new power, or level or whatever, they had to pay him. He made a lot of real money until he got caught. Fast forward ten years, and he had a new captive audience: an 18-year old with huge dreams and impressionability. The first night we met he asked me to close my eyes. What is it you want most? he asked. A recording deal, I said. And there we had it. The setting for a new make-believe. Almost two years later, he would write me a goodbye letter. He wouldn't apologize for the lying but he would say I'm sorry for trying to embellish the mundane.

day 21

confessions of a belly dancing sofa

I'm impatient to get to the next part of the story. I want to laugh about it now. I love to laugh. When I was younger, I watched a lot of sitcoms where the kid does something funny and everyone laughs. One time at dinner I thought I would try it. I exaggeratedly blew on the food in front of me and waited for everyone to laugh. They did not, and I got spit everywhere.

My friend made me laugh the most. I don't know
what it was. Maybe we shared the same humor,
maybe he knew it. It was on March 3rd of 2018,
around 3am. We were celebrating a friend's
birthday. I was in a silly mood. I was smiling so
much. He kept making me laugh harder. In front
of everyone, he told me he was especially
attracted to me when I was like this. When people
started leaving he came and sat next to me on the
couch. He was my closest friend. I don't doubt a
part of me liked it. But a much bigger part did not.
He told me what he wanted in my ear. It's funny
how physical dread can be. And it's funny I
wasn't prepared for what was coming next. I'd
heard about it many times before. I'd never
believed it. I'd been his cruelest defender. Now,
alone in the room with him. Nothing was making
sense. I froze. And I couldn't stop laughing.

day 22

confessions of a belly dancing sofa

After the band split, I tried to keep the friends I
knew would be lost. I didn't realize the more I
explained the crazier I sounded. The grand total
was two friends. They knew without me saying
anything. They both have A names like the rest of
my family. It's a cute little god detail.

Sometimes your finger is on the stove and you feel
it a little too late. I can't blame the people back
then for working with the information they had.
When the very bad thing happened, I didn't feel it
right away. It was by someone I clearly loved. I
said I liked it, there was proof. I tried to explain
once I realized. At that point it was a little too late.
I wouldn't have believed me, either. Innocent
when proven innocent. That's a law of the land
and it's a fair one. The thing is, it doesn't have to
end there. There's no double jeopardy in real life.
There's no deadline to redeem yourself. Cut out
the people who don't believe you. You'll make
new friends. Some of the old ones may even come
back. The wound will heal if you nurse it, or leave
it, or whatever. There are so many ways to heal.
You're already healthy enough to handle it.

day 23

confessions of a belly dancing sofa

The magic of it all isn't lost on me. He was big
into the occult. He'd freak out if he missed a night
of astral-projection because he was protecting
humankind from monsters in another dimension.
Also, we weren't allowed to talk about it. He once
licked blood off a cut on my arm to bond the two
of us. And his favorite number was 333.

3am on the 3rd day of the 3rd month. I told so many therapists. I wasn't here to see them because of what he did that night. I was here because I couldn't get him out. Out of context, I'd experienced worse transgressions. But my brain had gotten diseased. I felt permeated by him. After he left my life, everything he'd ever told me remained. I thought everyone was out to get me. I believed only he could save me. This is the last day about him, because I've forgiven him completely. He was afraid of the monsters in his head. It was clearly all a big metaphor.

day 24

confessions of a belly dancing sofa

When I was sick, the issue wasn't that I hated myself. It was that I liked myself too much. I believed I was above other people. Part of that mentality came from my experience those two years. I was in a group that was convinced we were going to save the world with our music. I thought I, personally, would save the world.

It's not productive to think you're special. It's paralyzing. It's like standing at the bottom of a mountain and thinking you're already at the top. You can't take a step because as soon as you do, you have to admit you're not where you thought. An ego trip to nowhere.

day 25

confessions of a belly dancing sofa

I was never trained. I used to think it was
something to brag about. You never had
lessons? You're a natural talent. I skated on it
for so long. My bandmates were playing the
music, so I didn't have to. Then, I was alone.
And I couldn't do it without them. I had so
many excuses. I screamed at my dad for not
putting me in music lessons as a kid. I blamed
my friends for not telling me enough that I
should keep singing.

There's a dating concept that applies here. If someone gives you mixed signals, or doesn't text back, you have to remind yourself. If they wanted to, they would. We give people excuses when we like them. They're probably busy, they implied that once. Maybe they didn't see their phone. We have to find some way to explain it because we're afraid of the real reason. Here's what it is. If I really wanted to pursue music. If I really loved it enough to do it alone. I would.

day 26

As I near the end, I have to wonder. Maybe this is all about my ego. Maybe I want people to know how much life I've lived. About a year after everything happened, I went on a first date. It didn't go well. I was a shell. I tried to talk him into it by telling him how great I used to be. Desperation, low self-worth, and living in the past. I had become the holy trinity of unattractive. I went home for winter and cried every single day. I couldn't get out of bed, I kept hitting my head. I knew it was a catalyst. I couldn't live like this anymore. I had to let it go.

I started making these belly dancing tutorials. I called it Belly Dancing Sofa. I filmed them alone, at 4am when I couldn't sleep. They were silly, sometimes satirical. I didn't care if people never saw them. I was making myself laugh. I was excited about something again. A long time ago, I started this journey to find my personal treasure. I thought I knew what that was. I was wrong. The answer was in front of me the whole time. It's not music. It's not even success. It's just me.

day 27

confessions of a belly dancing sofa

The thing I hated most about music was the self-promotion. It didn't come naturally to me. It felt like pulling teeth. I was in a thesis film my last year of college. I wrote the music, recorded it, and performed. I did a good job, I got my star moment. None of it felt good or right. It was directed by an ex-boyfriend who knew about my situation. He asked me, what if something comes from this? What if someone finds you?

I love music with all my heart. But I've never worked hard at it. There's something I like more. I've been reading since I could walk. My parents bring up a poem I wrote in second grade every time we have guests over. And I've been writing this in my head for three years. That's why it comes so easily. That's why I don't have trouble promoting it. I'm not a singer who can write. I'm a writer with a really good voice.

day 28

confessions of a belly dancing sofa

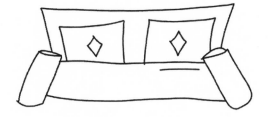

There are so many people I wish I could talk about. My dad, a dreamer like me. My mom, who has her own story to write. My friends who taught me everything I know. And then there's a bunch of randoms. Like this one female comedian, my junior year RA, a boy from my hometown, my favorite professor, my second grade teacher, my high school track coach, and the guy who waves when I walk into my favorite store. All of them had a hand in making this ending possible, regardless of if they ever see it.

I won't lie. It takes a village. But at night,
everyone's asleep. You'll have to do it yourself.
I'm not going to leave you without some advice.
Stop focusing so hard on your problems. Put on
a sexy song and move your hips to it. Throw
your body around. Make yourself laugh. And
just when you get distracted, even for a second.
That was happiness, if only for a second.

day 29

It rained yesterday. I used to hate the rain so much. Not too long ago I was in the middle of an ocean, gasping and tired. I wasn't drowning but I was close. And now I'm so far from there. Of course, I worry about the future. I could have a bad dream, it could all come back. I don't think it'll ever leave completely. I'm starting to think that's a really good thing.

As for the dreams, there's nothing more that can haunt me. I've already gotten it all out. So I'm going to enjoy this one. I can't stop looking out the window and smiling. The rain looks so good. I think I'm going to go outside. A fresh start, a fresh start, a fresh start.

day 30

confessions of a belly dancing sofa

I want to finish this right. I keep catching my
breath. I'm experiencing some resistance. I took
my songbook off the shelf and read it for the
first time in a while. I used to use it like a diary.
When I was sick I wrote I have to run without
stopping to greatness. I don't know where that is
I only see a stupid cliff. In high school, I wrote a
really knowing poem about hope. It was about
how it's as reliable as the sun. I was right. Hope
is not dreaming of impossible things. It's the
opposite. It's making a tiny little house out of
paper and being so pleased with how it turns out
that you want to make it out of wood.

I am not a mystery. I am not intimidating, or
very rock-and-roll. I'm not a savior, and I don't
have a mission. I have much more than that. I
have my body and my mind. I won't heal the
world with my voice. I will simply write a
couple paragraphs a day. If I'm pleased with
how they turn out, I can make it out of paper. If
it's bad, I can throw it away. I can make
something new. I will always be okay. A month
ago, I finally finished a song. I didn't do it
because it was my purpose. I had no audience.
No expectations when I came back. I just felt
like writing.

Sahfa Aboudkhil

confessions of a belly dancing sofa

Sahfa Aboudkhil

acknowledgments

Aya Aboudkhil, Amira Aboudkhil,
Alexandra Eftimie, Ava Lalezarzadeh,
Wiame Samaki, Yazmin Renteria,
Yasmeen Kaina, Sarah El Massry,
Alyssa Brostowin, Dina Al Jibori,
Naazley Boozari, Madelyn Chen
Scott Abramson, Alexis Victoria,
Jonathan Sarker, Katarina Guillot,
Brian Johnson, Miguel Caracheo,
Larry Toney, Daniela Castaneda,
Ruben Gutierrez, Vaibhav Aggarwal,
Raaghav Bageshwar, Ricky Niño,
David Baraza, Rigo Tovar, and anyone else
who contributed to the loving production of this
book.

Sahfa Aboudkhil

confessions of a belly dancing sofa

Sahfa Aboudkhil

ABOUT THE AUTHOR

Sahfa Aboudkhil has a degree in Comparative Literature from UCLA. She spent her time in school writing mediocre papers, playing halfhearted rock and roll, and ignoring her impending carpal tunnel syndrome. When she was younger she liked poetry, and in college she liked songwriting. Now she writes something in between. Her blog, *Confessions of a Belly Dancing Sofa*, is both her first public work and her first book. It can be found at bellydancingsofa.wordpress.com.